CLASSIC TELEV

*To Ashley,
enjoy!,
[signature]*

CLASSIC TELEVISION MADNESS

2022

A publication of

QUIET CREEK PUBLISHING

CLASSIC TELEVISION MADNESS!

CLASSIC TELEVISION MADNESS!

Copyright ©2022 Quiet Creek Publishing

Conceived, designed and written by Louis D. Lavalle

All rights reserved.

Published by Quiet Creek Publishing, Bradenton, Florida 34212

ISBN: 978-1-7350754-3-3 (print)

Printed in the United States of America

THIS LOGBOOK IS THE PROPERTY OF:

NAME _____

ADDRESS _____

_____

PHONE NUMBER _____

EMAIL _____

OTHER _____

_____

_____

IT WAS STARTED ON

_____

AND COMPLETED ON

_____

QUIET CREEK PUBLISHING

CLASSIC TELEVISION MADNESS!

THE PREMIER TELEVISION JOURNAL NOTEBOOK FOR OLDTIME CLASSIC TELEVISION LOVERS.

WHO DOESN'T LOVE *I Love Lucy*? Or *The Honeymooners*? Surely you remember *The Flintstones*? Or how about *Bewitched*? Those were the days of black and white TV, remember? These shows and may others were classics, and we watched them during influential times, some sad, and some joyous. And guess what? Most of them were family-friendly, from a simpler time.

Classic Television Madness captures these shows and many more from the last 70 years, the Fifties, Sixties, shows like *The Dick Van Dyke Show* with Mary Tyler Moore (1961-1966); *Bewitched* and *The Beverly Hillbillies,* both from 1964-1971. **Classic Television Madness** (from the publishers of Movie Time Madness) helps you remember when television was fun to watch, was wholesome and provided weekly entertainment for millions of TV viewers. You'll relive the old years and discover many facts about long-forgotten TV shows and the actors that starred in them.

Many of these memorable series' sported distinctive lead characters who played legendary roles and spoke classic lines .... i.e., *"One shot, to the moon, Alice,"* etc. **Classic Television Madness** is the premier television journal notebook for oldtime classic television lovers. What makes this journal special is the unique television pages, with hints and clues to the quiz questions. So it's much more than a journal!

The television trivia quizzes appear at the top of every other righthand page. These fact-based clues will test your knowledge of past television shows and cast members. (Of course the answers are listed in the back of the book!)

The whole family will have fun trying to solve the quizzes. How about a sample quiz question or two? #1: *Who was considered Mr. Television?* #2: *Irene Dunn was the star of what 50's TV series?* You'll have to guess the answers on your own, or read the book!

Remembering the oldies but goodies!

CLASSIC TELEVISION MADNESS!

GENRES

Need help deciding on the genre of your TV show?
Here's a comprehensive list that will help you.

Inspiring	Offbeat
Cerebral	Ominous
Psychological	Dark
Suspenseful	Thriller
Exciting	Rousing
Romantic	Gritty
Drama	Mysterious
Soupy	Violent
Emotional	Military
Intimate	Epic
Steamy	Royalty
Rauncy	Period Piece
Irrevelant	Relaxing
Slick	Docuseries
Campy	Comedy

QUIET CREEK PUBLISHING

CLASSIC TELEVISION MADNESS!

Start your exciting adventure into
reliving the oldies but goodies
from oldtime television!

This notebook will be your "go-to" source for
answers to your questions about your favorite
television shows, the stars, the air dates, actors
and other things you may have forgotten.
Use it often—
it's your personal journal!

Have fun with the quizzes at the top of every
right hand page! All you need
is a pen and a good memory!

NOTE: Answers to Quizzes are on pages 157 - 162

QUIET CREEK PUBLISHING

CLASSIC TELEVISION MADNESS!

NOTES AND OBSERVATIONS

Who who played Ethel Mertz in the network TV sitcom "I Love Lucy"?

HINT:

YOUR ANSWER:

CLASSIC TELEVISION MADNESS!

NOTES AND OBSERVATIONS

Who co-starred with Dick Van Dyke in this CBS family comedy from 1961-1966?

HINT:

YOUR ANSWER:

CLASSIC TELEVISION MADNESS!

NOTES AND OBSERVATIONS

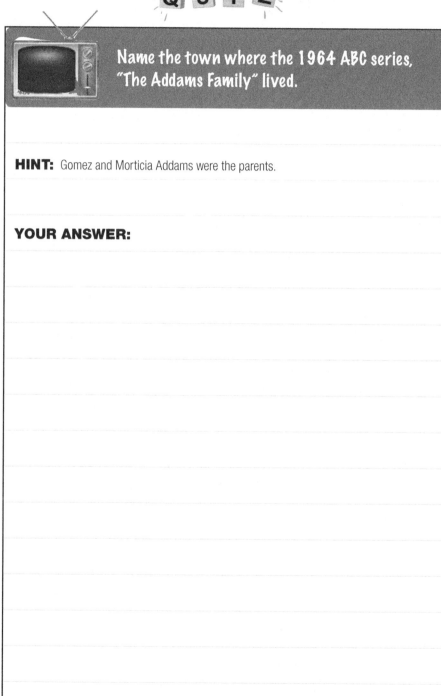

Name the town where the 1964 ABC series, "The Addams Family" lived.

HINT: Gomez and Morticia Addams were the parents.

YOUR ANSWER:

CLASSIC TELEVISION MADNESS!

NOTES AND OBSERVATIONS

 *"Those Were the Days"* was the opening theme music for what 1979 TV series?

HINT: Jean Stapleton played the piano and sang it with Carroll O'Connor.

YOUR ANSWER:

CLASSIC TELEVISION MADNESS!

NOTES AND OBSERVATIONS

"What is the name of the company that produced the 1951 CBS series "I Love Lucy"?

HINT: Lucille Ball's husband's first name was part of the title.

YOUR ANSWER:

CLASSIC TELEVISION MADNESS!

NOTES AND OBSERVATIONS

What was the name of Dick Clarks' television program?

HINT:

YOUR ANSWER:

CLASSIC TELEVISION MADNESS!

NOTES AND OBSERVATIONS

 What actor played the lead in the 1979 NBC TV sitcom "It's All in the Family"?

HINT: His stage name was Archie Bunker.

YOUR ANSWER:

CLASSIC TELEVISION MADNESS!

NOTES AND OBSERVATIONS

Ed Asner, Gavin MacLeod and Valerie Harper were the co-stars of what 1970 CBS TV series?

HINT: Betty White joined the cast midway into its run.

YOUR ANSWER:

CLASSIC TELEVISION MADNESS!

NOTES AND OBSERVATIONS

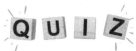

Who was the emcee of "American Bandstand" ?

HINT: This TV star also emceed "New Year's Rocking 'Eve"

YOUR ANSWER:

CLASSIC TELEVISION MADNESS!

NOTES AND OBSERVATIONS

What CBS 1948 show was hosted by "Mr. Television?"

HINT: Texaco was the sponsor, later Buick took over .

YOUR ANSWER:

CLASSIC TELEVISION MADNESS!

NOTES AND OBSERVATIONS

 **Who said: "Don't do the crime if you can't do the time."?**

HINT: "Lala" the cockatoo was a cast member

YOUR ANSWER:

CLASSIC TELEVISION MADNESS!

NOTES AND OBSERVATIONS

Who was the star of the ABC 1975 sitcom, "Barney Miller?"

HINT: Abe Vigoda played "Fish" in this series.

YOUR ANSWER:

CLASSIC TELEVISION MADNESS!

NOTES AND OBSERVATIONS

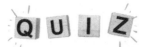

Who was the emcee of the 1950 CBS TV hit game show "Beat the Clock?"

HINT: His first name was Bud.

YOUR ANSWER:

CLASSIC TELEVISION MADNESS!

NOTES AND OBSERVATIONS

Name the lead character in the 1965 NBC sitcom "I Dream of Jeannie."

HINT: The premier episode was titled "Lady in the Bottle."

YOUR ANSWER:

CLASSIC TELEVISION MADNESS!

NOTES AND OBSERVATIONS

 **Who starred in the 1948 CBS drama "I Remember Mama"?**

HINT: Marta Hanson was her character name.

YOUR ANSWER:

CLASSIC TELEVISION MADNESS!

NOTES AND OBSERVATIONS

Who were the four main characters in the 1975 CBS series "The Honeymooners?"

HINT: First letter of each actor's first name: J, A, J, A

YOUR ANSWER:

CLASSIC TELEVISION MADNESS!

NOTES AND OBSERVATIONS

What CBS TV detective was always seen with with a lollipop?

HINT: His nickname was Kojak.

YOUR ANSWER:

CLASSIC TELEVISION MADNESS!

NOTES AND OBSERVATIONS

Was this dog actor male or female?

HINT: Lassie was the name of the canine.

YOUR ANSWER:

CLASSIC TELEVISION MADNESS!

NOTES AND OBSERVATIONS

Who were the two female stars of Laverne & Shirley?

HINT: The show started its run on CBS in 1976.

YOUR ANSWER:

CLASSIC TELEVISION MADNESS!

NOTES AND OBSERVATIONS

Who played the two leads in the 1964 CBS series "The Man From U.N.C.L.E.?"

HINT: One character's stage name was Napoleon Solo.

YOUR ANSWER:

CLASSIC TELEVISION MADNESS!

NOTES AND OBSERVATIONS

Who was the head writer for the "Dick Van Dyke Show?"

HINT: He also acted in the series.

YOUR ANSWER:

CLASSIC TELEVISION MADNESS!

NOTES AND OBSERVATIONS

What was the stage name for Eddie Andersen, Jack Benny's butler?

HINT: His name is the same as an upstate NY town.

YOUR ANSWER:

NOTES AND OBSERVATIONS

A trenchcoat and an old Mercedes were the hallmarks of what TV detective?

HINT: The show name was Columbo.

YOUR ANSWER:

CLASSIC TELEVISION MADNESS!

NOTES AND OBSERVATIONS

Who said "Baby, you're the greatest" on CBS TV in 1955?"

HINT: Do you really need one?

YOUR ANSWER:

CLASSIC TELEVISION MADNESS!

NOTES AND OBSERVATIONS

 **What was Art Carney's stage name?**

HINT: The 1951 sitcom was "The Honeymooners." He worked for the City sewer department.

YOUR ANSWER:

CLASSIC TELEVISION MADNESS!

NOTES AND OBSERVATIONS

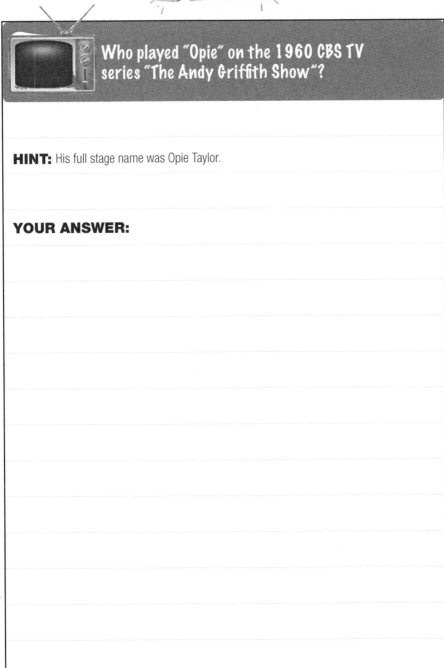

Who played "Opie" on the 1960 CBS TV series "The Andy Griffith Show"?

HINT: His full stage name was Opie Taylor.

YOUR ANSWER:

CLASSIC TELEVISION MADNESS!

NOTES AND OBSERVATIONS

This actor played a witch with magic powers on this ABC family comedy from 1964-1972.

HINT: The show was "Bewitched."

YOUR ANSWER:

CLASSIC TELEVISION MADNESS!

NOTES AND OBSERVATIONS

Rod Serling was the lead character in what 1959 TV series?

HINT: Burgess Meredith and Jack Klugman appeared in 4 episodes

YOUR ANSWER:

CLASSIC TELEVISION MADNESS!

NOTES AND OBSERVATIONS

Who played the female lead character in the 1969 CBS TV series "The Brady Bunch"?

HINT: Her first name: Maureen.

YOUR ANSWER:

CLASSIC TELEVISION MADNESS!

NOTES AND OBSERVATIONS

 ## Who played the male lead in the CBS TV 1979 sitcom "All in the Family"?

HINT: Sally Struthers also starred in the series.

YOUR ANSWER:

CLASSIC TELEVISION MADNESS!

NOTES AND OBSERVATIONS

Complete the title "Laverne & _____"

HINT: Penny Marshall played the character LaVerne.

YOUR ANSWER:

CLASSIC TELEVISION MADNESS!

NOTES AND OBSERVATIONS

Name the two lead actors from the 1966 NBC series "Star Trek: The Original Series".

HINT: Their first names were William and Leonard.

YOUR ANSWER:

CLASSIC TELEVISION MADNESS!

NOTES AND OBSERVATIONS

A 1994 TV series about Stone Age families. What was the name of the show?

HINT: Fred, Betty, Barney and Wilma were the couples' first names.

YOUR ANSWER:

CLASSIC TELEVISION MADNESS!

NOTES AND OBSERVATIONS

Isabel Sanford and Sherman Hemsley starred in what 1985 CBS series?

HINT: The theme song was "Movin' On Up"

YOUR ANSWER:

CLASSIC TELEVISION MADNESS!

NOTES AND OBSERVATIONS

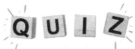

Suzanne Pleshette played against what psychologist male actor in this 1972 show?

HINT: He was the star of The Bob Newhart Show

YOUR ANSWER:

CLASSIC TELEVISION MADNESS!

NOTES AND OBSERVATIONS

Seven men and women were stranded on what island in this 1964 CBS sitcom?

HINT: Their charter boat never made it to its destination.

YOUR ANSWER:

CLASSIC TELEVISION MADNESS!

NOTES AND OBSERVATIONS

Who was the "Caped Crusader" from 1966 television??

HINT:

YOUR ANSWER:

CLASSIC TELEVISION MADNESS!

NOTES AND OBSERVATIONS

QUIZ

"Leave It to _____"? CBS TV 1957

HINT: Hugh Beaumont and Barbara Billingsley were cast members.

YOUR ANSWER:

CLASSIC TELEVISION MADNESS!

NOTES AND OBSERVATIONS

What detective was famous for the line "Just the facts m'am, just the facts"?

HINT: His stage name was Joe Friday.

YOUR ANSWER:

CLASSIC TELEVISION MADNESS!

NOTES AND OBSERVATIONS

This nouveau riche family moved to Beverly Hills in 1971 and did it their way.

HINT: Their family name was The Clampetts.

YOUR ANSWER:

CLASSIC TELEVISION MADNESS!

NOTES AND OBSERVATIONS

Name the 1955 CBS TV series of short stories about crime of every description.

HINT: Most episodes opened with the dialogue, "Good evening..."

YOUR ANSWER:

CLASSIC TELEVISION MADNESS!

NOTES AND OBSERVATIONS

 The everyday life of this couple raising their two sons, Ricky and David.

HINT: This 1952 ABC series featured a real-life married couple.

YOUR ANSWER:

CLASSIC TELEVISION MADNESS!

NOTES AND OBSERVATIONS

Fred MacMurray, a widower, is left to raise his three sons with the help of his father-in-law in this 1951 CBS series.

HINT: Read between the above lines for the clue.

YOUR ANSWER:

CLASSIC TELEVISION MADNESS!

NOTES AND OBSERVATIONS

 Name the 1964 CBS sitcom about a family of friendly monsters led by Fred Gwynne's character.

HINT: Their home address was 1313 Mockingbird Lane.

YOUR ANSWER:

CLASSIC TELEVISION MADNESS!

NOTES AND OBSERVATIONS

Who was the male lead in the 1954 series (it aired on three networks) "Father Knows Best"?

HINT: The stage name for the character was Jim Andersen.

YOUR ANSWER:

CLASSIC TELEVISION MADNESS!

NOTES AND OBSERVATIONS

"The Donna _____ Show." (ABC, 1958)

HINT: Her husband was a pediatrician.

YOUR ANSWER:

CLASSIC TELEVISION MADNESS!

NOTES AND OBSERVATIONS

This 1995 CBS science-fiction show starred Bob Johnson, Ben Wright, William Douglas and Robert Culp.

HINT: The opening line in each episode was "*There is nothing wrong with your televison set.*"

YOUR ANSWER:

CLASSIC TELEVISION MADNESS!

NOTES AND OBSERVATIONS

 The Daily Planet was the newspaper of record for this 1952 CBS TV series.

HINT: Lois Lane was a main character. BUT, it's NOT a one word answer!

YOUR ANSWER:

CLASSIC TELEVISION MADNESS!

NOTES AND OBSERVATIONS

Larry Hagman finds a bottle containing a female genie. Name the 1970 NBC Show.

HINT:

YOUR ANSWER:

NOTES AND OBSERVATIONS

Marlo Thomas was what girl in this 1966 ABC sitcom?

HINT: Her father was a beloved American actor, singer, nightclub comedian and producer.

YOUR ANSWER:

NOTES AND OBSERVATIONS

Alan Lane and his talking horse starred in this 1961 CBS TV comedy.

HINT: "A _____ is a _____, of course, of course, and no one can talk to a _____, of course."

YOUR ANSWER:

CLASSIC TELEVISION MADNESS!

NOTES AND OBSERVATIONS

This collie stole the hearts of America every week in this 1954 CBS series.

HINT:

YOUR ANSWER:

CLASSIC TELEVISION MADNESS!

NOTES AND OBSERVATIONS

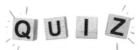

A family of pop musicians entertained us every week in 1974 on ABC.

HINT: "A _____ in a pear tree."

YOUR ANSWER:

NOTES AND OBSERVATIONS

Who was the character that played the role of Dennis the _____. (1993)

HINT: His last name was North.

YOUR ANSWER:

CLASSIC TELEVISION MADNESS!

NOTES AND OBSERVATIONS

Vinnie Barbarino led this gang of high school misfits nicknamed the Sweathogs. Name the 1975 ABC sitcom.

HINT: Freddie Washington is the hip black student known as the athletic Sweathog.

YOUR ANSWER:

CLASSIC TELEVISION MADNESS!

NOTES AND OBSERVATIONS

Three single girls share an apartment in Santa Monica, California in this 1984 ABC comedy show.

HINT: John Ritter was the male cast member.

YOUR ANSWER:

CLASSIC TELEVISION MADNESS!

NOTES AND OBSERVATIONS

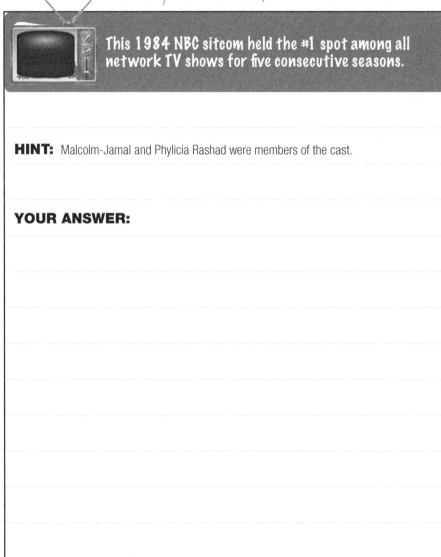

This 1984 NBC sitcom held the #1 spot among all network TV shows for five consecutive seasons.

HINT: Malcolm-Jamal and Phylicia Rashad were members of the cast.

YOUR ANSWER:

CLASSIC TELEVISION MADNESS!

NOTES AND OBSERVATIONS

Name the ranch in Virginia City, Nevada where this family western was located. (NBC 1959)

HINT: The family name was The Cartwrights. The show: Bonanza.

YOUR ANSWER:

CLASSIC TELEVISION MADNESS!

NOTES AND OBSERVATIONS

Three beautiful women worked in this 1976 ABC crime drama series as investigators.

HINT: This show ushered in the phrase "jiggle TV."

YOUR ANSWER:

CLASSIC TELEVISION MADNESS!

NOTES AND OBSERVATIONS

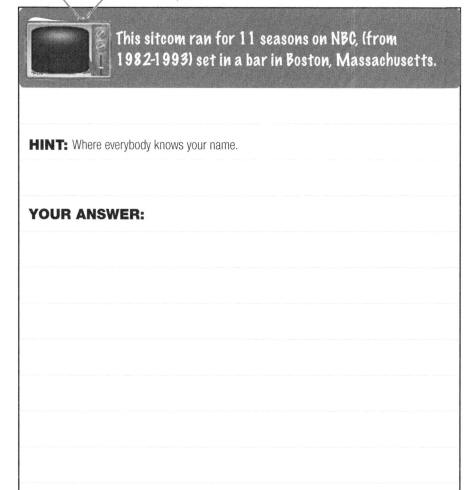

This sitcom ran for 11 seasons on NBC, (from 1982-1993) set in a bar in Boston, Massachusetts.

HINT: Where everybody knows your name.

YOUR ANSWER:

CLASSIC TELEVISION MADNESS!

NOTES AND OBSERVATIONS

A fictional Marine Preserve in southern Florida was the setting for this 1964 NBC series starring a lovable dolphin.

HINT:

YOUR ANSWER:

CLASSIC TELEVISION MADNESS!

NOTES AND OBSERVATIONS

An ex-cop, a pesky Jack Russell terrier and perky live-in supported this radio show host in this 2004 NBC sitcom that takes place n Seattle.

HINT: Jane Leeves played Daphne in this series.

YOUR ANSWER:

CLASSIC TELEVISION MADNESS!

NOTES AND OBSERVATIONS

These four widowed women lived their golden years in the Florida sun. The 1985 sitcom aired on NBC.

HINT:

YOUR ANSWER:

CLASSIC TELEVISION MADNESS!

NOTES AND OBSERVATIONS

Arthir "Fonzie" Fonzarelli starred in what ABC sitcom that aired from 1974 to 1984?

HINT: Henry Winkler also starred in this series.

YOUR ANSWER:

NOTES AND OBSERVATIONS

 Alan Alda starred in this medical-military-comedy 1972 CBS series in fictional South Korea.

HINT: Major Margaret "Hot Lips" Houlihan was the character played by Loretta Swit.

YOUR ANSWER:

NOTES AND OBSERVATIONS

James "Sonny" Crockett and Ricardo "Rico" Tubbs were the stars of this 1984 NBC crime drama series.

HINT: James "Sonny" Crockett was played by Don Johnson.

YOUR ANSWER:

NOTES AND OBSERVATIONS

 The "IMF" was a small team of secret agents that used clever disguises to to capture crime lords. The drama aired in 1996 on CBS.

HINT: Barbara Bain, Peter Graves and Greg Morris were cast members.

YOUR ANSWER:

NOTES AND OBSERVATIONS

Bill Bixby starred in this 1963 CBS sci-fi sitcom that began after the discovery of a crashed spaceship.

HINT: Ray Walston played the lead character.

YOUR ANSWER:

CLASSIC TELEVISION MADNESS!

NOTES AND OBSERVATIONS

Candice Bergen starred as an investigative reporter in this sitcom that aired from **1988** to **1998** on CBS.

HINT: She was the star reporter for "FYI", a news magazine.

YOUR ANSWER:

CLASSIC TELEVISION MADNESS!

NOTES AND OBSERVATIONS

Two mis-matched divorced men share a Manhattan apartment in this 1970 ABC sitcom.

HINT: Their stage names were Felix and Oscar.

YOUR ANSWER:

CLASSIC TELEVISION MADNESS!

NOTES AND OBSERVATIONS

The host of this late night NBC TV show from the 50's shared the spotlight with Don Knotts, Louis Nye, Tom Poston and Gene Rayburn, among others.

HINT: He wore glasses and played piano.

YOUR ANSWER:

CLASSIC TELEVISION MADNESS!

NOTES AND OBSERVATIONS

The Beatles and Elvis Presley first appeared on this prime time variety show. It aired from 1948 to 1971 on CBS.

HINT: "We have a r-e-a-l-l-y big show tonight" (pronounced "shew"!)

YOUR ANSWER:

CLASSIC TELEVISION MADNESS!

NOTES AND OBSERVATIONS

CLASSIC TELEVISION MADNESS!

NOTES AND OBSERVATIONS

ANSWERS, p11- 41

Page	Answer	TV Show/Characters
11	Vivian Vance	*I Love Lucy* - Desi Arnez, Lucille Ball, William Frawley, Keith Thibodeaux, Shirley Mitchell, Mary Jane Croft, Doris Singleton, Kathryn Card, Frank Nelson, Bob Jellison, Elizabeth Patterson
13	Mary Tyler Moore	*The Dick Van Dyke Show* - Rose Marie, Morey Amsterdam, Larry Mathews, Carl Reiner, Jerry Paris, Richard Deacon, Ann Morgan Guilbert, Peter Oliphant, Ray Romano, Jack C. Flippen
15	Cemetery	*The Addams Family* - John Astin, Carolyn Jones, Ted Cassidy, Lisa Loring, Jackie Coogan, Blossom Rock
17	*All in the Family*	(See page 69)
19	DesiLu Productions	*I Love Lucy* (See page 11)
21	*American Bandstand*	Dick Clark
23	Carroll O'Connor, Archie Bunker	(See page 69)
25	*The Mary Tyler Moore Show*	Ed Asner, Gavin MacLeod, Ted Knight, Valerie Harper, Betty White Cloris Leachman, Georgia Engel, John Amos, Lisa Gerritsen, Joyce Bulifant, Nancy Walker
27	Dick Clark	*American Bandstand*
29	Milton Berle	*The Milton Berle Show* - Carol Burnett, Arnold Stang, Ruth Gilbert, Red Skelton, Donna Loren, Bobby Rydell, Irving Benson, Ed Herlihy, Billy May
31	Robert Blake	*Baretta* - Tom Ewell, Lala the Cockatoo, Michael D. Roberts, Dana Elcar, Edward Grover, Chino Williams, Angelo Rossitto, Ron Thompson, Paul Lichtman, Shelley Duvall, Richard Cox
33	Hal Linden	*Barney Miller* - Max Gail, Ron Glass, Steve Landesberg, Jack Soo, Ron Carey, Abe Vigoda, Danny Arnold, James Gregory, Gregory Sierra, Barbara Barrie, George Murdock
35	Bud Collyer	*Beat The Clock* - Monty Hall, Jack Narz, Tom Dreesen, Richard Kline, Randi Oakes, Roxie Roker, Leslie Ackerman, Robert Mandan, Tamara Dobson
37	Barbara Eden	*I Dream of Jeannie* - Larry Hagman, Bill Daily, Hayden Rorke, Emmaline Henry, Michael Ansara, Farrah Fawcett, Vinton Hayworth, Barton MacLane, Paul Lynde, Dabney Coleman, Karen Sharpe
39	Irene Dunn	*I Remember Mama* - Oskar Homolka, Barbara Bel Geddes, Ellen Corby, Philip Dorn, Cedric Hardwicke, Edgar Bergen, Barbara O'Neil, Rudy Vallee, Florence Bates, Edith Evanson, Hope Landin
41	Jackie Gleason, Audrey Meadows, Art Carney, Joyce Randolph	

CLASSIC TELEVISION MADNESS!

ANSWERS, p43 - p73

Page	Answer	TV Show/Characters
43	Telly Savalas	*Kojak* - Kevin Dobson, George Savalas, Dan Frazer, Vince Conti, Roger Robinson, Dan Frazer
45	Lassie was a male dog.	
47	Penny Marshall and Cindy Williams	*Laverne & Shirley* - David L. Lander, Michael McKean, Phil Foster, Eddie Mekka, Betty Garrett, Vicki Lawrence, Harry Shearer, Kenneth Mars, Carole Ita White, Leslie Easterbrook
49	Robert Vaughn, David McCallum	*The Man from UNCLE* - Leo G. Carroll, Sharon Tate, Barbara Feldon, William Shatner
51	Carl Reiner	*The Dick Van Dyke Show* (See page 13)
53	Jack Benny	*The Jack Benny Show* - Don Wilson, Eddie Anderson, Dennis Day, Mel Blanc, Mary Livingstone, Frank Nelson, Benny Rubin, Phil Harris, Artie Auerbach, Bob Crosby
55	Peter Falk	*Columbo* - Shera Danese, Patrick McGoohan, Robert Culp, Jack Cassidy, William Shatner, Vera Miles, Mike Lally, Bruce Kirby, Martin Sheen, Vincent Price, John Finnegan
57	Jackie Gleason	*The Honeymooners* - Audrey Meadows, Joyce Randolph, Art Carney, Jack Lescoulie, Pert Kelton, Jane Kean, Sheila MacRae
59	Ed Norton	*The Honeymooners* (see above)
61	Ron Howard	*The Andy Griffith Show* - Andy Griffith, Don Knotts, Ron Howard, Frances Bavier, Colin Male, Howard McNear, Aneta Corsaut, Betty Lynn, Jim Nabors, George Lindsey, Hal Smith, Elinor Donahue
63	Elizabeth Montgomery	*Bewitched* - Elizabeth Montgomery, Dick York, Erin Murphy, Alice Pearce. Marion Lorne, Paul Lynde, David Lawrence, Kasey Rogers,, Diane Murphy
65	*The Twilight Zone*	Rod Sterling, William Shatner, Robert McCord, Vaughn Taylor, Morgan Brittany, Inger Stevens
67	Florence Henderson	*The Brady Bunch* - Maureen McCormick, Susan Olsen, Barry Williams, Eve Plumb, Mike Lookinland, Robert Reed, Ann B. Davis, Robbie Rist, Allan Melvin, Jack Collins
69	Carroll O'Connor	*All in The Family* - Sally Struthers, Jean Stapleton, Rob Reiner, Danielle Brisebois, Bea Arthur, Mike Evans, Sherman Hemsley, Liz Torres, Allan Melvin, Isabel Sanford, Jason Wingreen
71	Shirley	(see page 47)
73	William Shatner, Leonard Nimoy	*Star Trek: The Original Series* - Nichelle Nichols, DeForest Kelley, George Takei, James Doohan, Gene Roddenberry, Walter Koenig, Majel Barrett, Bill Blackburn, Grace Lee Whitney, Eddie Paskey

 **ANSWERS, p75 - p97**

Page	Answer	TV Show/Characters
75	*The Flintstones*	Alan Reed, Mel Blanc, Jean Vander, Harvey Korman, John Goodman, Rick Moranis, Elizabeth Taylor, Elizabeth Perkins, Halle Berry, Kyle MacLachlan, Don Messick, Bea Benaderet Jean Vander Pyl, Gerry Johnson, Henry Corden
77	*The Jeffersons*	Isabel Sanford, Sherman Helmsley, Marla Gibbs, Roxie Roker, Mike Evans, Berlinda Tolbert, Paul Benedict, Zara Cully, Damon Evans, Franklin Cover, Jay Hammer, Andrew Rubin
79	Bob Newhart	*The Bob Newhart Show* - Peter Bonerz, Bill Daily, Suzanne Pleshette, Marcia Wallace, Jack Riley, Florida Friebus, Tom Poston, John Fiedler, Renée Lippin, Larry Gelman, Pat Finley
81	*Gilligan's Island*	Dawn Wells, Bob Denver, Tina Louise, Alan Hale Jr., Russell Johnson, Jim Backus, Natalie Schafer, Zsa Zsa Gábor, Edward ` Faulkner, Glenn Langan, Rory Calhoun, Nancy McCarthy
83	*Batman*	Adam West, Burt Ward, Alan Napier, Neil Hamilton, Julie Newmar, Eartha Kitt, Cesar Romero, Yvonne Craig, Burgess Meredith, Leslie Gore, Bruce Lee, Lee Merriweather, Cliff Robertson
85	*Leave It To Beaver*	Jerry Mathers, Hugh Beaumont, Barbara Billingsley, Tony Dow, Ken Osmond, Frank Bank, Rusty Stevens, Stanley Fafara, Stephen Talbot, Rich Correll, Jeri Weil, Sue Randall
87	Jack Webb	*Dragnet* - Ben Alexander, Olan Soule, Vic Perrin, Harry Morgan, Scatman Crothers, Edward Faulkner
89	*The Beverly Hillbillies*	Buddy Ebsen, Donna Douglas, Irene Ryan, Max Baer Jr., Buddy Ebsen, Nancy Culp, Raymond Bailey, Bea Benaderet, Harriet MacGibbon, Sharon Tate, Larry Pennell, Louis Nye, Linda Kaye Henning
91	*Alfred Hitchcock Presents*	Harry Tyler, John Williams, Patricia Hitchcock, Alan Napier, Russell Collins, John Williams, Percy Helton, Vera Miles, Phyllis Thaxter, Raymond Bailey, Walther Mathau, Phillip Coolidge, Cloris Leachman
93	*The Adventures of Ozzie & Harriet*	Ozzie Nelson, Harriet Nelson, David Nelson, Ricky Nelson Skip Young, Don DeFore, Constance Harper, June Blair, Mary Jane Croft, Kristin Nelson, Lyle Talbot, Parley Baer
95	*My Three Sons*	Fred MacMurray, Stanley Livingston, Tim Considine, William Demarest, William Frawley, Don Grady, Barry Livingston, Tina Cole, Ronne Troup, Dawn Lyn, Beverly Garland, Meredith MacRae
97	*The Munsters*	Fred Gwynne, Al Lewis, Yvonne De Carlo, Butch Patrick, Pat Priest, Beverley Owen, John Carradine, Chet Stratton, Dom DeLuise, Walter Woolf King, Mike Mazurki, Roger C. Carmel

CLASSIC TELEVISION MADNESS!

 **ANSWERS, p101 - 123**

Page	Answer	TV Show/Characters
101	*The Donna Reed Show*	Donna Reed, Paul Petersen, Carl Betz, Shelley Fabares, Patty Petersen, Darryl Richard, Jimmy Hawkins, Candy Moore, Ann McCrea, Bob Crane, Tommy Ivo
103	*The Outer Limits*	Robert Culp, William Shatner, Barbara Rush, Vic Perrin, Mariion Ross, John Hoyt
105	*The Adventures of Superman*	George Reeves, Noel Neill, Jack Larson, John Hamilton, Robert Shane, Bill Kennedy, John Hamilton, Thomas Carr, Joi Lansing, Billy Gray, Paul Burke, John Beradino, Hugh Beaumont
107	*I Dream Of Jeannie*	Barbara Eden, Bill Daily, Hayden Rorke, Larry Hagman, Hayden Rorke, Emmaline Henry, Michael Ansara, Farrah Fawcett, Vinton Hayworth, Barton MacLane, Paul Lynde, Dabney Coleman, Karen Sharpe
109	*That Girl*	Marlo Thomas, Ted Bessell, Lew Parker, Bernie Kopell, Rosemary DeCamp, Bonnie Scott
111	Mister Ed	Alan Young, Connie Hines,, Edna Skinner, Larry Keating, Allan Lane, Bamboo Harvester (Mister Ed), Florence MacMichael, Leon Ames, Donna Douglas, Sharon Tate, Jack Kruschen, Barry Kelley
113	*Lassie*	Tommie Rettig, John Provost, June Lockhart, Hugh Reilly, Cloris Leachman, George Cleveland, Jed Allan, Larry Pennell, Joey D. Vieira, Karl Swenson, Robert Bray
115	*The Partridge Family*	Shirley Jones, David Cassidy, Susan Dey, Danny Bonaduce, Suzanne Crough, Brian Foster, Dave Madden, Jeremy Gelbwaks Ray Bolger, Mark Hamill, Slim Pickens, Ricky Segall
117	*Dennis the Menace*	Herbert Anderson, Jay North, Gloria Henry, Billy Booth, Joseph Kearns, Sylvia Field
119	*Welcome Back, Kotter*	Gabe Kaplan, John Travolta, Ron Palillo, Marcia Strassman, Robert Hegyes, John Sylvester, Lawrence Hilton-Jacobs, Debralee Scott, Stephen Shortridge, Melonie Haller, Dennis Bowen
121	*Three's Company*	Jack Ritter, Suzanne Somers, Joyce DeWitt, Richard Kline, Don Knotts, Priscilla Barnes, Jenilee Harrison, Audra Lindley, Norman Fell, Ann Wedgeworth, Paul Ainsley, Jordan Charney
123	*The Cosby Show*	Bill Cosby, Phylicia Rashad, Michael Jamal Warner, Tempestt Bledsoe, Lisa Bonet, Kesha Knight Pulliam, Sabrina Beauf, Geoffrey Owens, Raven-Symone, Earle Hyman, Deon Richmond, Reno Wilson

 **ANSWERS, p125 - p149**

Page	Answer	TV Show/Characters
125	The Ponderosa Ranch	*Bonanza* - Lorne Green, Pernell Roberts, Dan Blocker, Michael Landon, Victor Sen Yung, David Canary, Mitch Vogel, Ray Teal, Bing Russell, Tim Matheson, Guy Williams, Harry Holcombe
127	*Charlie's Angels*	Jaclyn Smith, Cheryl Ladd, Kate Jackson, John Forsythe, Farrah Fawcett, David Doyle
129	*Cheers*	Ted Danson, Shelley Long, Woody Harrelson, Rhea Parlman, Kirstie Alley, George Wendt, Kelsey Grammer, Nicholas Colasanto, Bebe Neuwirth, John Ratzenberger, Leah Remini, Jackie Swanson
131	*Flipper*	Brian Kelly, Luke Halpin, Tommy Norden, Andy Devine, Ulla Stromstedt, Barbara Feldon, Denise Nickerson, Dan White, Burt Reynolds, Flipper
133	*Frasier*	Kelsey Grammer, Jane Leeves, David Hyde Pierce, Peri Gilpin, John Mahoney, Enzo the Dog, Dan Butler, Bebe Neuwirth, Jean Smart, Wendie Malick, Moose, Trevor Einhorn, Harriet Sansom Harris
135	*The Golden Girls*	Bea Arthur, Rue McClanahan, Betty White, Estelle Getty, Herb Edelman, Debbie Reynolds, Harold Gould, Deena Freeman, Nancy Walker, Doris Belack, Richard Mulligan, Bill Dana
137	*Happy Days*	Ron Howard, Henry Winkler, Tom Bosley, Marion Ross, Anson Williams, Donny Most, Erin Moran, Scott Baio, Pat Morita, Lynda Goodfriend, Ted McGinley, Al Molinaro
139	*M*A*S*H*	Alan Alda, Loretta Swit, Gary Burghoff, McLean Stevenson, William Christopher, Jamie Farr, Harry Morgan, Mike Farrell, Wayne Rogers, Harry Morgan, David Ogden Stiers, Larry Linville, Kellye Nakahara
141	*Miami Vice*	Don Johnson, Phillip Michael Thomas, Edward James Olmos, Michael Talbot, Olivia Brown, Saundra Santiago
143	*Mission: Impossible*	Steven Hill, Peter Graves, Barbara Bain, Greg Morris, Peter Lupus, Martin Landau, Leonard Nimoy, Bob Johnson
145	*My Favorite Martian*	Ray Walston, Bill Bixby, Pamela Britton, Alan Hewitt, Ann Marshall, J. Pat O'Malley
147	*Murphy Brown*	Candice Bergen, Charles Kimbrough, Joe Regalbuto, Faith Ford, Grant Shaud, Pat Corley, Robert Pastorelli, Jake McDorman, Nik Dodani, Lily Tomlin, Tyne Daly, Jay Thomas
149	*The Odd Couple*	Tony Randall, Jack Klugman, Al Molinaro, Gary Walberg, Larry Gelman, Garry Marshall, Penny Marshall, Monica Evans, Elinor Donahue, Garry Walberg, Brett Somers, Janis Hansen, Joan Hotchkis

CLASSIC TELEVISION MADNESS!

 **ANSWERS, p151 - 153**

Page	Answer	TV Show/Characters
151	The Steve Allen Show	Steve Allen, Louis Nye, Don Knotts, Tom Poston, Gene Rayburn, Dayton Allen, Jimmie Rogers, Skitch Henderson, Tim Conway, Les Brown
153	The Ed Sullivan Show	Ed Sullivan, Ralph Paul, Art Hannes, Dinah Shore, Charo, Sally Forrest, Lauritz Melchoir, Bern Bennett

ATTENTION: If you have discovered errors, misspellngs, ommisions, etc., in any information presented in this journal, we welcome your feedback. You can email comments to quietcreekpublishing.com. Thank you!

Love this book?
Don't forget to leave a review!

Every review matters, and it matters a lot!
Go to the website and click the "REVIEWS" tab.

OTHER BOOKS AND JOURNALS FROM
QUIET CREEK PUBLISHING

"Millie! A Love Story" (a memoir)

"Millie! The Last Chapters" (a follow-up memoir)

PAPERBACK JOURNALS

"My Journal - A Log for All My Books"
(for book lovers)

"Movie Time Madness" (for movie lovers)

"Music Madness" (coming soon)
(for music lovers)

For more information and book
descriptions or to order
visit www.quietcreekpublishing.com

ABOUT THE AUTHOR

Louis David Lavalle

LOUIS STARTED WRITING SOON after he was accepted at Brooklyn Technical High School in the Fort Greene section of Brooklyn. From more than 600 students who applied, he and a friend were the only two accepted. The year was 1955. He enjoyed the engineering classes especially and actively wrote papers on the many facets of engineering, industrial manufacturing and particularly mechanical drawing.

His teenage years were marked by the family's several relocations between Portsmouth, NH, Marshalltown, Iowa, Central Islip, Long Island, in addition to his early years in East Elmhurst, Queens, where he attended P.S. 127 Elementary School.

Each change of address required a change of school, culminating in his graduation from Jamaica High School in Queens, NY.

His interest in printing began in Portsmouth where, at the age of 15, he worked as a stonehand and press operator; his experience in typography blossomed, eventually becoming the foundation for

a career in graphic design. He was able to put his growing talent in writing and design to advantage working for commercial printers in New Hyde Park, LI, and later New York City.

In the early 70s his writing and graphic experience was put to good use when he formed an advertising agency, working from a home office. Several years later he was invited to work at a local ad agency in Northport, LI as senior account manager.

He left the agency for a production position in a New York City brokerage firm. The temptation to be his own boss led him to form a commercial print brokerage company in 1985, serving Manhattan businesses, which continues to operate today.

He has designed and produced hundreds of corporate identity symbols and branding guidelines, including a trade display and video for a national client. His years of experience allowed him to expand the company to offer printing and fulfillment services to the business and non-profit sectors.

He has written extensively for clients in the sales promotional sector, including company letters, brochures and presentations and creative briefs.

Louis partnered with his wife Roseanne to write "Millie! A Love Story" in 2019 and this newly-released, follow-up book, "Millie! The Last Chapters" this year.

The couple live in Bradenton, Florida.

QUIET CREEK PUBLISHING

Made in the USA
Columbia, SC
24 April 2022